New Testament Bible Knowledge Game

by Shery Koons Borenstein

gameboard by Gary Hoover

Cover by Gary Hoover

Copyright © 1994

Shining Star Publications

ISBN No. 0-382-30483-7

Standardized Subject Code TA ac

Printing No. 987654321

Shining Star Publications
1204 Buchanan St., Box 299
Carthage, IL 62321-0299

Unless otherwise indicated, the New International Version of the Bible was used in preparing the activities of this book.

DEDICATION

To my loving husband, Jim.
Your support allows me to minister to others
in unusual and marvelous ways!
Only eternity will reveal what God has wrought
through *our* willings hearts and hands.

Special Appreciation
To those who worked on the editing, graphics, and
designing of this book.

SS3842

PURPOSE OF THE GAME

The purpose of the game is to have fun while learning and reinforcing general Bible knowledge of the following areas:

- Bible people
- Basic content
- New Testament parables
- Important events
- Key New Testament places
- Scripture phrases and short passages

OBJECT OF THE GAME

The object of *New Testament Bible Knowledge Game* is to be the first person to arrive at the New Jerusalem. Through answering the question cards and moving the appropriate spaces, any player can be the winner!

GAME PARTS

GAMEBOARD

Carefully remove and unfold the gameboard from the center of this book. To make the gameboard more sturdy, mount the paper on a heavier board and laminate it or cover it with clear adhesive plastic. (Note: Using Spray Mount™ artist's adhesive is a neat and simple method for mounting the gameboard.)

QUESTION CARDS

NewTestament Bible Knowledge Game contains 252 New Testament Question cards–also referred to as Bible Question cards in the directions. Each card contains a Bible question, Scripture reference (where the answer can be found), the correct answer, and the number of spaces awarded for the response. On the reverse side of the card, players will notice a category from which the Bible question has been taken.

The cards may be separated by cutting along the solid lines. To allow for more durability, laminate each page before cutting the cards.

"FREE TRAVEL" CARDS

There are nine of these cards included with the question cards. These cards may be redeemed in order to progress along the game path in spite of giving an incorrect answer. These should also be laminated before cutting.

GAME TOKENS

You will need a game token for each player or team. Follow the directions on page 6 for making these tokens or use buttons, coins, bottle caps, or similar items.

GAME INSTRUCTIONS

Make a copy of the game rules (pages 4-5) to place with the game pieces.

CONTAINER

Store your gameboard, cards, instructions, and tokens in a box or large Ziploc™ Storage Bag.

GAME INSTRUCTIONS

RULES FOR PLAY

1. Place the gameboard on a flat surface, such as a table or the floor. Mix the Bible Question cards and place them in a stack beside the board.

2. Each player selects a game token.

3. Each player chooses a card from the stack to see who will go first. The player choosing a Bible Question card with the highest space value begins the game. Return the cards to the bottom of the stack.

   •If a player chooses a Free Travel card, he may keep the card for future play and pick another card for its space value.

   •In a tie situation, these players choose again.

4. The first player chooses a card. Without looking at the card, the player hands it to the person on his left. That player reads the Bible question aloud to him. The answer and number of spaces awarded, found at the bottom of the card, is checked by the reader.

   •If the player answers the question correctly, he is allowed to advance his game token the designated number of spaces.

   •If he answers incorrectly, he may not move his token, and the person on his left gets a turn.

5. Once a player's token is on the gameboard and he gives an incorrect answer, the player may choose to redeem one of his Free Travel cards.

   •To redeem a Free Travel card the player must show the card to the other players and say that he wants to use his card in place of the Bible Question card he just missed. He returns his Free Travel card to the bottom of the card stack.

   •Redeeming a Free Travel card allows the player to move forward the given number of spaces on his previously missed Bible Question card.

6. A player must always move the number of spaces shown on the card. The only exception to this rule is when the player arrives at the end of the path and chooses a card with a greater value of spaces than are left for his token to travel. He can then move past the final space by answering the question correctly–thus making him the winner!

7. Each Bible Question card is placed on the bottom of the stack after being drawn, whether answered correctly or incorrectly.

8. When a player chooses a Free Travel card, he keeps the card and chooses another card to answer.

9. A player landing on one of the Journey Ahead spaces continues his turn by moving his token ahead the same number of spaces just moved. For example, if he correctly answers a question card with three spaces, he moves the game token three spaces, landing on Journey Ahead space. He then moves his game token ahead three more spaces. (The space value of a card is doubled when the player lands on a space marked Journey Ahead.)

10. Any number of game tokens may occupy the same space at the same time.

11. The first player to get to the New Jerusalem wins the game.

12. The players determine how long they have to answer a question and how precise an answer must be. Time and accuracy may vary for each player. A reader may choose to cover the answer with his finger and show the question to the current player for clarification.

13. Bibles may be used for locating some or all of the answers.

   •When a teacher is supervising the game, she may determine how precise the answers are to be and whether or not Bibles may be used.

OTHER WAYS TO PLAY

1. Use the cards without the gameboard. Divide the group into two teams. Let the team players choose which category they wish to answer. Give points based on the number of spaces that would be awarded, only multiply them by ten (if they are valued at two spaces, award 20 points). Also, give an extra 50 points when a team member chooses a Free Travel card. (For an incorrect response, award zero points or subtract what points would have been awarded.) The winning team is the one with the most points at the end of the game.

2. Copy the category sheets on page 6. Give one to each player. Place the cards in separate category stacks. (Follow the normal procedure for choosing a beginning player.) The first player picks a card from the stack of his choice and gives it to the person on his left, who reads the question. If the player answers the question correctly, he places a check mark under the correct category on the sheet. If a player draws a Free Travel card from a stack, he may check any category he chooses. The first player to correctly answer three questions from each of the four categories wins. (This variation can be readily adapted for large group play.)

GAME TOKEN PATTERNS

1. Cut out each token on solid lines.
2. Fold on broken lines.
3. Glue the back flaps together to allow the game token to stand.

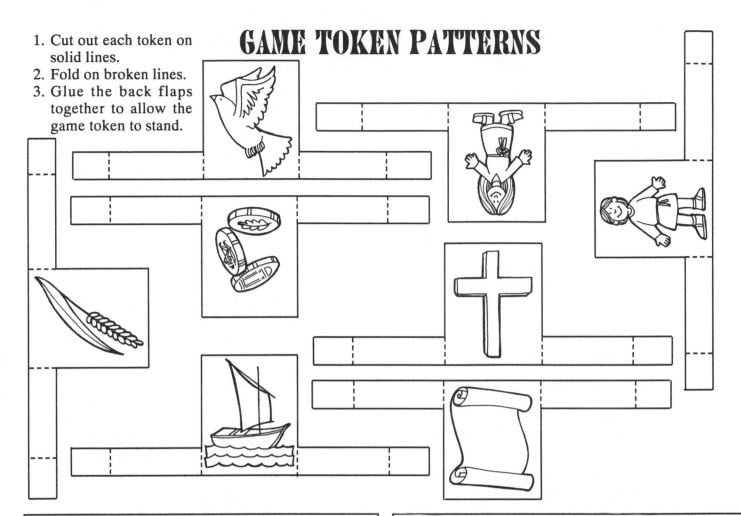

CATEGORY SHEET			
NUMBERS & EVENTS	PLACES & THINGS	BIBLE PEOPLE	PARABLES & QUOTES

CATEGORY SHEET			
NUMBERS & EVENTS	PLACES & THINGS	BIBLE PEOPLE	PARABLES & QUOTES

Check a square each time you correctly answer a question from that category. Check a box of your choice when you draw a Free Travel card.

Check a square each time you correctly answer a question from that category. Check a box of your choice when you draw a Free Travel card.

Shining Star Publications, Copyright © 1994

SS3842

QUESTION: According to Matthew 7:13, how many gates lead to destruction?

REFERENCE: Matthew 7:13
ANSWER: 1

SPACES AWARDED: 2

QUESTION: How many disciples did Jesus send out to minister to others?

REFERENCE: Matthew 10:1
ANSWER: 12

SPACES AWARDED: 1

QUESTION: What were the disciples doing on the Sabbath that made the Pharisees angry?
a. Eating grain in a field
b. Sleeping
c. Preaching to large crowds

REFERENCE: Matthew 12:1-2
ANSWER: a. Eating grain in a field

SPACES AWARDED: 2

QUESTION: How many men did Jesus feed with five loaves and two fish?

REFERENCE: Matthew 14:21
ANSWER: Five thousand

SPACES AWARDED: 3

QUESTION: One stormy evening on the lake, what did Peter ask Jesus to let him do?

REFERENCE: Matthew 14:28-29
ANSWER: Walk to Jesus on the water

SPACES AWARDED: 2

QUESTION: Jesus fed four thousand men with several fish and
a. five loaves of bread.
b. three loaves of bread.
c. seven loaves of bread.

REFERENCE: Matthew 15:34
ANSWER: c. seven loaves of bread

SPACES AWARDED: 3

QUESTION: At Jesus'
a. crucifixion
b. glorification
c. transfiguration
His face shone like the sun and His clothes became white as light.

REFERENCE: Matthew 17:2
ANSWER: c. transfiguration

SPACES 1

QUESTION: What did Jesus tell Peter to do to get money to pay their taxes?

REFERENCE: Matthew 17:27
ANSWER: Catch a fish and open its mouth to find a coin to pay the tax

SPACES AWARDED: 4

QUESTION: Give the number for the commandment that Jesus said was the greatest.

REFERENCE: Matthew 22:37-38
ANSWER: The first

SPACES AWARDED: 2

SS3842

SS3842

QUESTION: According to Matthew 10:29, how many sparrows are sold for a penny?

REFERENCE: Matthew 10:29
ANSWER: 2

SPACES AWARDED: 3

QUESTION: Why were the Pharisees upset with Jesus' disciples for picking and eating grain?

REFERENCE: Matthew 12:1-2
ANSWER: They were doing it on the Sabbath.

SPACES AWARDED: 4

QUESTION: According to Matthew 18:20, how many Christians gathered in God's name will cause Him to be with them?

REFERENCE: Matthew 18:20
ANSWER: 2 or 3

SPACES AWARDED: 3

QUESTION: Jesus said those who gave up much to serve Him would receive eternal life and
a. twice as much.
b. a thousand times more.
c. a hundred times more.

REFERENCE: Matthew 19:29
ANSWER: c. a hundred times more

SPACES AWARDED: 2

QUESTION: True or False–The angels in heaven know when Jesus will return to earth.

REFERENCE: Matthew 24:36
ANSWER: False

SPACES AWARDED: 3

QUESTION: How many foolish virgins were there in the parable of the ten virgins?

REFERENCE: Matthew 25:2
ANSWER: 5

SPACES AWARDED: 2

QUESTION: In Matthew 25, one servant was given five talents. How many more talents did he gain?

REFERENCE: Matthew 25:16
ANSWER: 5

SPACES AWARDED: 3

QUESTION: For how many silver coins did Judas turn Jesus over to the chief priests?

REFERENCE: Matthew 26:14-15
ANSWER: 30

SPACES AWARDED: 4

QUESTION: What Jewish feast was held shortly before Jesus' crucifixion?

REFERENCE: Matthew 26:18
ANSWER: Passover

SPACES AWARDED: 4

SS3842

SS3842

QUESTION: How many times did Peter deny knowing Jesus before the rooster crowed?

REFERENCE: Matthew 26:75
ANSWER: 3

SPACES AWARDED: 3

QUESTION: True or False—False witnesses came to accuse Jesus before the Sanhedrin.

REFERENCE: Matthew 26:60
ANSWER: True

SPACES AWARDED: 2

QUESTION: How many robbers were crucified along with Jesus?

REFERENCE: Matthew 27:38
ANSWER: 2

SPACES AWARDED: 1

QUESTION: What happened to the curtain of the temple the moment Jesus died?

REFERENCE: Matthew 27:51-54
ANSWER: It was torn from top to bottom.

SPACES AWARDED: 3

QUESTION: What lie were the soldiers told to tell after Jesus rose from the grave?

REFERENCE: Matthew 28:12-15
ANSWER: That disciples stole Jesus' body while the soldiers were asleep.

SPACES AWARDED: 4

QUESTION: How many days was Jesus in the wilderness being tempted by Satan?

REFERENCE: Mark 1:13
ANSWER: 40

SPACES AWARDED: 3

QUESTION: Why did Jesus often get up early in the morning and go to a place alone?

REFERENCE: Mark 1:35
ANSWER: He wanted to pray.

SPACES AWARDED: 3

QUESTION: How did four men get a paralyzed man through the crowd to Jesus?

REFERENCE: Mark 2:2-4
ANSWER: They lowered him through the roof.

SPACES AWARDED: 3

QUESTION: Jesus allowed a legion of demons to enter
a. 200 pigs.
b. 2000 pigs.
c. 20 pigs.

REFERENCE: Mark 5:12-13
ANSWER: b. 2000 pigs

SPACES AWARDED: 2

11

SS3842

SS3842

QUESTION: What did the disciples do after the Lord's Supper before going to the Mount of Olives?
a. Prayed
b. Ate
c. Sang

REFERENCE: Mark 14:26

ANSWER: c. Sang

SPACES AWARDED: 2

QUESTION: For how long did Jesus ask His disciples to keep watch for Him while He prayed in Gethsemane?

REFERENCE: Mark 14:37

ANSWER: 1 hour

SPACES AWARDED: 3

QUESTION: How old was Jesus when His parents took Him to Jerusalem to celebrate the Passover?

REFERENCE: Luke 2:41-42

ANSWER: 12

SPACES AWARDED: 4

QUESTION: How many coins did the poor widow place in the temple offering?

REFERENCE: Mark 12:42

ANSWER: 2

SPACES AWARDED: 3

QUESTION: True or False—The lesson of the poor widow's offering is to give what we can, whether it's much or little.

REFERENCE: Mark 12:44

ANSWER: True

SPACES AWARDED: 2

QUESTION: The expensive perfume a woman poured on Jesus' feet could have been sold for how much money?

REFERENCE: Mark 14:5

ANSWER: More than a year's wages

SPACES AWARDED: 3

QUESTION: How old was Jairus' daughter when Jesus healed her?

REFERENCE: Mark 5:42

ANSWER: 12

SPACES AWARDED: 3

QUESTION: Jesus sent out the twelve disciples __ by __. (What numbers go in the blanks?)

REFERENCE: Mark 6:7

ANSWER: 2 by 2

SPACES AWARDED: 2

QUESTION: Jesus said that after ___ days He would rise from the dead.

REFERENCE: Mark 10:34

ANSWER: 3

SPACES AWARDED: 2

SS3842

QUESTION: The crippled beggar whom Peter healed was over
a. thirty years old.
b. twenty years old.
c. forty years old.

REFERENCE: Acts 4:22
ANSWER: c. forty years old

SPACES AWARDED: 2

QUESTION: What did the people do to Stephen when they took him outside the city?

REFERENCE: Acts 7:58
ANSWER: Stoned him

SPACES AWARDED: 3

QUESTION: For how many days was Saul blind from seeing the light from heaven?

REFERENCE: Acts 9:9
ANSWER: 3

SPACES AWARDED: 4

QUESTION: How many fish were in the net Peter dragged ashore in John 21:11?
a. 153
b. 1000
c. 734

REFERENCE: John 21:11
ANSWER: 153

SPACES AWARDED: 4

QUESTION: How many times did Jesus ask Peter, "Do you love Me?"

REFERENCE: John 21:15-17
ANSWER: 3

SPACES AWARDED: 3

QUESTION: True or False–Peter gave silver and gold to the crippled beggar outside the temple gate.

REFERENCE: Acts 3:6
ANSWER: False

SPACES AWARDED: 2

QUESTION: What time of day did Mary and the others visit Jesus' tomb?

REFERENCE: Luke 24:1
ANSWER: Very early in the morning

SPACES AWARDED: 3

QUESTION: The leftovers from the feeding of the five thousand filled how many baskets?

REFERENCE: John 6:13
ANSWER: 12

SPACES AWARDED: 4

QUESTION: How did Jesus teach His disciples a lesson on being a servant? (Hint: He used a basin of water.)

REFERENCE: John 13:5
ANSWER: He washed their feet.

SPACES AWARDED: 3

SS3842

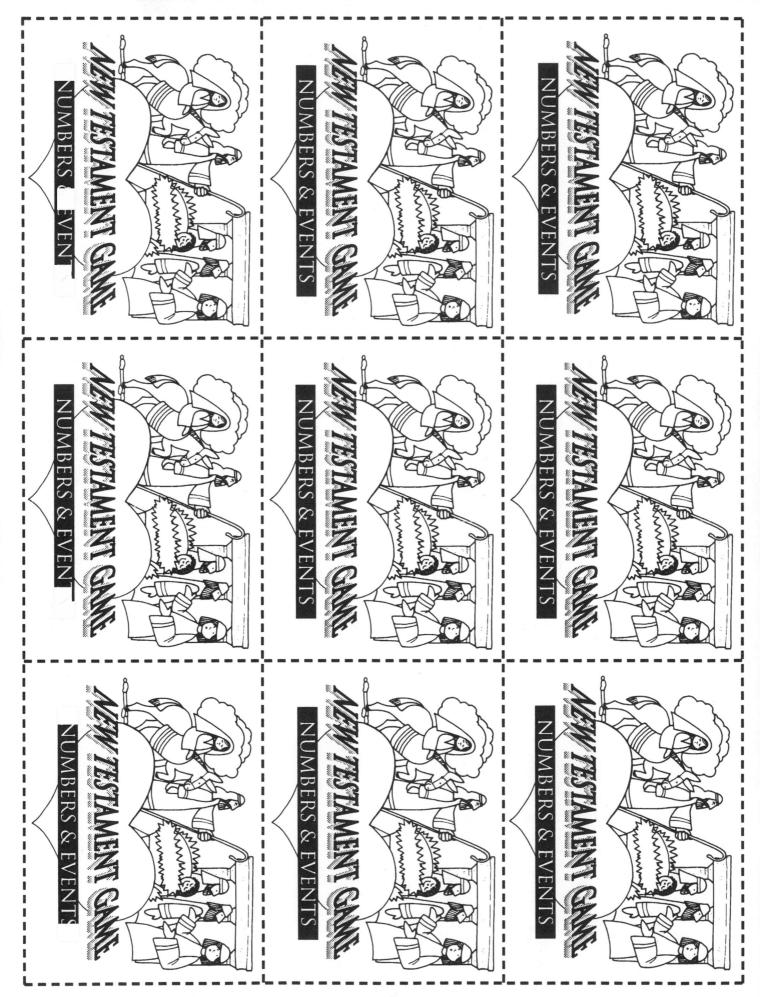

Shining Star Publications, Copyright © 1994

SS3842

QUESTION: According to Philippians 4:4, how often should Christians "rejoice in the Lord"?

REFERENCE: Philippians 4:4
ANSWER: Always

SPACES AWARDED: 1

QUESTION: How many times did Jesus sacrifice Himself to take away our sins?

REFERENCE: Hebrews 9:28
ANSWER: One time

SPACES AWARDED: 2

QUESTION: How often did Bible-time priests offer sacrifices?

REFERENCE: Hebrews 10:11
ANSWER: Day after day (again and again)

SPACES AWARDED: 2

QUESTION: How many men were with Paul on the ship to Rome?
a. 325
b. 400
c. 276

REFERENCE: Acts 27:37
ANSWER: c. 276

SPACES AWARDED: 3

QUESTION: For how many years did Paul live in a rented house in the city of Rome?

REFERENCE: Acts 28:30
ANSWER: 2

SPACES AWARDED: 3

QUESTION: According to Ephesians 6:2, which commandment has a promise included with it?
a. The first
b. The sixth
c. The ninth

REFERENCE: Ephesians 6:2
ANSWER: a. The first

SPACES AWARDED: 2

QUESTION: What time was it when Paul and Silas sang in prison?

REFERENCE: Acts 16:25
ANSWER: About midnight

SPACES AWARDED: 3

QUESTION: How long did Paul stay to teach the people in the city of Corinth?

REFERENCE: Acts 18:11
ANSWER: $1\frac{1}{2}$ years

SPACES AWARDED: 4

QUESTION: What happened to Eutychus when he fell asleep as Paul preached?

REFERENCE: Acts 20:9-10
ANSWER: He fell out of the window.

SPACES AWARDED: 3

SS3842

QUESTION: For how long will Jesus reign in heaven?

REFERENCE: Revelation 11:15
ANSWER: Forever

SPACES AWARDED: 2

QUESTION: How many gates are there in the Holy City? (Hint: The names of the tribes of Israel are written on them.)

REFERENCE: Revelation 21:12
ANSWER: 12

SPACES AWARDED: 3

QUESTION: How many foundations does the wall of the New Jerusalem have? (Hint: The names of the apostles are written on them.)

REFERENCE: Revelation 21:14
ANSWER: 12

SPACES AWARDED: 2

QUESTION: How many angels did John see standing at the four corners of the earth, holding back the four winds?

REFERENCE: Revelation 7:1
ANSWER: 2

SPACES AWARDED: 1

QUESTION: How many trumpets were the seven angels in Revelation 8 holding?

REFERENCE: Revelation 8:6
ANSWER: 7

SPACES AWARDED: 2

QUESTION: According to Revelation 11:3, how many witnesses clothed in sackcloth will prophesy for 1260 days?

REFERENCE: Revelation 11:3
ANSWER: 2

SPACES AWARDED: 3

QUESTION: True or False–The sacrifices offered by Bible-time priests always took away people's sins.

REFERENCE: Hebrews 10:11
ANSWER: False

SPACES AWARDED: 2

QUESTION: The "faith" chapter of the Bible which lists people who had great faith is
a. Hebrews 7.
b. Hebrews 11.
c. John 10.

REFERENCE: See the book of Hebrews.
ANSWER: Hebrews 11

SPACES AWARDED: 3

QUESTION: How many seals did the Lamb open in the book of Revelation?

REFERENCE: Revelation 6:1
ANSWER: 7

SPACES AWARDED: 3

Shining Star Publications, Copyright © 1994

SS3842

SS3842

QUESTION: Who was the man who preached to prepare for Jesus' coming? (Hint: He also baptized Jesus.)

REFERENCE: Matthew 3:1-2, 13-15
ANSWER: John the Baptist

SPACES AWARDED: 3

QUESTION: Who tempted Jesus in the desert?

REFERENCE: Matthew 4:1
ANSWER: The devil (Satan)

SPACES AWARDED: 3

QUESTION: Who was the tax collector Jesus called to be His disciple?

REFERENCE: Matthew 9:9
ANSWER: Matthew

SPACES AWARDED: 4

QUESTION: Who obeyed God's command to name His Son Jesus?

REFERENCE: Matthew 1:24-25
ANSWER: Joseph

SPACES AWARDED: 2

QUESTION: Name two of the first four men that Jesus called to become His disciples.

REFERENCE: Matthew 4:18, 21
ANSWER: Simon Peter, Andrew, James, and John

SPACES AWARDED: 4

QUESTION: Name one of the two Old Testament saints who appeared with Jesus at His transfiguration.

REFERENCE: Matthew 17:3
ANSWER: Moses or Elijah

SPACES AWARDED: 2

QUESTION: Which New Testament king wanted to kill the baby Jesus?

REFERENCE: Matthew 2:16
ANSWER: King Herod

SPACES AWARDED: 3

QUESTION: Because the man with leprosy believed, what happened when Jesus touched him?

REFERENCE: Matthew 8:3
ANSWER: He was healed.

SPACES AWARDED: 1

QUESTION: Which of Jesus' disciples betrayed Him?

REFERENCE: Matthew 26:48-49
ANSWER: Judas

SPACES AWARDED: 3

SS3842

22

SS3842

QUESTION: Which group of religious leaders gave a tenth of their spices, but neglected the important matters of the law?

REFERENCE: Matthew 23:23
ANSWER: The Pharisees

SPACES AWARDED: 4

QUESTION: Which disciple made a pact with the chief priests to betray Jesus?
a. Peter
b. James
c. Judas

REFERENCE: Matthew 26:14
ANSWER: c. Judas

SPACES AWARDED: 2

QUESTION: Which disciple denied that he was a follower of Jesus?
a. Judas
b. Peter
c. James

REFERENCE: Matthew 26:33-35
ANSWER: b. Peter

SPACES AWARDED: 2

QUESTION: When Jesus asked, "Whom do you say I am?" who answered, "You are . . . the Son of the living God."?

REFERENCE: Matthew 16:15-16
ANSWER: Simon Peter

SPACES AWARDED: 4

QUESTION: When asked about paying taxes, Jesus showed a coin to the Pharisees. Whose picture was on the coin?

REFERENCE: Matthew 22:20-21
ANSWER: Caesar's

SPACES AWARDED: 4

QUESTION: According to Matthew 22:39, whom should you love as you love yourself?

REFERENCE: Matthew 22:39
ANSWER: Your neighbor

SPACES AWARDED: 3

QUESTION: Name two of Jesus' earthly brothers.

REFERENCE: Matthew 13:55
ANSWER: James, Joseph, Simon, or Judas

SPACES AWARDED: 4

QUESTION: Who had enough faith to try to walk to Jesus on the water?

REFERENCE: Matthew 14:28-31
ANSWER: Peter

SPACES AWARDED: 3

QUESTION: In Matthew 15, which Old Testament prophet did Jesus quote?
a. Jeremiah
b. Hosea
c. Isaiah

REFERENCE: Matthew 15:7-9
ANSWER: c. Isaiah

SPACES AWARDED: 2

SS3842

SS3842

QUESTION: Who was the prisoner released in place of Jesus?

REFERENCE: Matthew 27:21-22
ANSWER: Barabbas

SPACES AWARDED: 4

QUESTION: Who handed Jesus over to be crucified?

REFERENCE: Matthew 27:24-26
ANSWER: Pilate

SPACES AWARDED: 4

QUESTION: Who provided a new tomb in which to bury Jesus' body?

REFERENCE: Matthew 27:57
ANSWER: Joseph of Arimathea

SPACES AWARDED: 3

QUESTION: Who removed the stone from Jesus' tomb?

REFERENCE: Matthew 28:2
ANSWER: An angel

SPACES AWARDED: 2

QUESTION: Name one of the women who went to Jesus' tomb and found the stone rolled away!

REFERENCE: Matthew 28:1-7
ANSWER: Mary Magdalene or the other Mary

SPACES AWARDED: 2

QUESTION: Which Old Testament prophet wrote that John the Baptist would prepare the way for Jesus?
a. Isaiah
b. Ezekiel
c. Hosea

REFERENCE: Mark 1:2-4
ANSWER: a. Isaiah

SPACES AWARDED: 2

QUESTION: Who said he was not worthy to untie Jesus' sandals?
a. Isaiah
b. Joseph
c. John the Baptist

REFERENCE: Mark 1:6-7
ANSWER: c. John the Baptist

SPACES AWARDED: 3

QUESTION: Whose mother-in-law did Jesus heal of a fever?
a. Simon's
b. James'
c. John's

REFERENCE: Mark 1:30-31
ANSWER: a. Simon's

SPACES AWARDED: 3

QUESTION: What job did Levi have when Jesus called him to be His disciple?

REFERENCE: Mark 2:14
ANSWER: He was a tax collector.

SPACES AWARDED: 4

SS3842

Shining Star Publications, Copyright © 1994

SS3842

QUESTION: Name one of the brothers whom Christ renamed 'Sons of Thunder.' (Hint: They were His disciples.)

REFERENCE: Mark 3:17
ANSWER: James or John

SPACES AWARDED: 3

QUESTION: Who cried out to the wind and the waves, "Quiet! Be still!"?

REFERENCE: Mark 4:39
ANSWER: Jesus

SPACES AWARDED: 2

QUESTION: Jesus healed Jairus'
a. daughter.
b. mother.
c. son.

REFERENCE: Mark 5:35-42
ANSWER: a. daughter

SPACES AWARDED: 2

QUESTION: Who was celebrating his birthday the night John the Baptist was beheaded?

REFERENCE: Mark 6:21-25
ANSWER: Herod

SPACES AWARDED: 3

QUESTION: Whom did men sometimes call the "Son of Man" or the "Son of David"?

REFERENCE: Mark 10:45, 48
ANSWER: Jesus

SPACES AWARDED: 1

QUESTION: Jesus warned Christians to watch out for false ___ who would perform signs and miracles to deceive them.

REFERENCE: Mark 13:22-23
ANSWER: prophets

SPACES AWARDED: 3

QUESTION: John the Baptist's father, Zechariah, was
a. a tent maker.
b. a priest.
c. an army captain.

REFERENCE: Luke 1:5
ANSWER: b. a priest

SPACES AWARDED: 2

QUESTION: Who was John the Baptist's mother?

REFERENCE: Luke 1:5
ANSWER: Elizabeth

SPACES AWARDED: 4

QUESTION: What angel told Zechariah that he would have a son?

REFERENCE: Luke 1:19
ANSWER: Gabriel

SPACES AWARDED: 4

SS3842

SS3842

QUESTION: What angel told Mary she would be the mother of Jesus?

REFERENCE: Luke 1:26-27
ANSWER: Gabriel

SPACES AWARDED: 3

QUESTION: True or False–John was named "John" after a relative.

REFERENCE: Luke 1:59-61
ANSWER: False

SPACES AWARDED: 2

QUESTION: Which of the twelve disciples owned a boat?
a. Luke
b. Matthew
c. Simon Peter

REFERENCE: Luke 5:3
ANSWER: c. Simon Peter

SPACES AWARDED: 2

QUESTION: Which sister was more concerned about household duties–Martha or Mary?

REFERENCE: Luke 10:40
ANSWER: Martha

SPACES AWARDED: 2

QUESTION: Which man was a tax collector?
a. Zechariah
b. Zacchaeus
c. Zephaniah

REFERENCE: Luke 19:2
ANSWER: b. Zacchaeus

SPACES 1

QUESTION: Jesus told Simon that he would be called Cephas. What's another name for Cephas?

REFERENCE: John 1:42
ANSWER: Peter

SPACES AWARDED: 2

QUESTION: True or False–Nicodemus was a Pharisee.

REFERENCE: John 3:9-10
ANSWER: True

SPACES AWARDED: 2

QUESTION: Who said He was the "bread of life"?

REFERENCE: John 6:35
ANSWER: Jesus

SPACES AWARDED: 2

QUESTION: Who is the "father of lies"?

REFERENCE: John 8:44
ANSWER: The devil (Satan)

SPACES 2

SS3842

SS3842

QUESTION: When the apostles were in prison, who came and opened the doors to let them out?
REFERENCE: Acts 5:19
ANSWER: An angel of the Lord
SPACES AWARDED: 3

QUESTION: Which apostle stood by, approving the stoning of Stephen?
REFERENCE: Acts 8:1
ANSWER: Saul (Paul)
SPACES AWARDED: 3

QUESTION: Who was God's "chosen instrument" to take the Gospel to the Gentiles?
REFERENCE: Acts 9:15-17
ANSWER: Saul (Paul)
SPACES AWARDED: 2

QUESTION: Whom did God send on the day of Pentecost to help Christians?
REFERENCE: Acts 2:1-4
ANSWER: The Holy Spirit
SPACES AWARDED: 3

QUESTION: True or False—Barnabas' name meant "Son of Encouragement."
REFERENCE: Acts 4:36
ANSWER: True
SPACES AWARDED: 2

QUESTION: What husband and wife lied to the Holy Spirit and kept part of their offering for themselves?
REFERENCE: Acts 5:1-4
ANSWER: Ananias and Sapphira
SPACES AWARDED: 4

QUESTION: Who cut off the right ear of Malchus, one of the soldiers who came to arrest Jesus?
REFERENCE: John 18:10
ANSWER: Simon Peter
SPACES AWARDED: 4

QUESTION: Who said he would have to touch the nail marks and place his hand on Jesus' side before he would believe Jesus was alive?
REFERENCE: John 20:24-25
ANSWER: Thomas
SPACES AWARDED: 2

QUESTION: Who was chosen by the eleven to replace Judas as the twelfth disciple?
REFERENCE: Acts 1:26
ANSWER: Matthias
SPACES AWARDED: 4

SS3842

SS3842

QUESTION: Who was the man who owned the slave Onesimus?

REFERENCE: Philemon 1:1, 10-11
ANSWER: Philemon

SPACES AWARDED: 4

QUESTION: Which man of faith was called "God's friend"?

REFERENCE: James 2:23
ANSWER: Abraham

SPACES AWARDED: 4

QUESTION: Who wrote in the book of Revelation what he saw and heard?

REFERENCE: Revelation 22:8
ANSWER: John

SPACES AWARDED: 3

QUESTION: Paul planted Gospel "seed" and Apollos watered it. Who made it grow?

REFERENCE: 1 Corinthians 3:6
ANSWER: God

SPACES AWARDED: 2

QUESTION: Who was whipped five times, beaten three times, stoned once, and shipwrecked three times?

REFERENCE: 2 Corinthians 11:24-25
ANSWER: Paul

SPACES AWARDED: 2

QUESTION: Who wrote the letters to the Thessalonians?

REFERENCE: 2 Thessalonians 3:17
ANSWER: Paul

SPACES AWARDED: 3

QUESTION: What type of work did Dorcas do?

REFERENCE: Acts 9:39
ANSWER: She made clothes.

SPACES AWARDED: 4

QUESTION: Who was so excited about Peter being set free from prison, she forgot to open the door to let him in?
a. Mary
b. Martha
c. Rhoda

REFERENCE: Acts 12:13-14
ANSWER: c. Rhoda

SPACES AWARDED: 3

QUESTION: What type of work did Aquila and Priscilla do?

REFERENCE: Acts 18:2-3
ANSWER: They made tents.

SPACES AWARDED: 4

SS3842

SS3842

QUESTION: What did Herodias' daughter ask King Herod to bring to her on a platter?

REFERENCE: Matthew 14:6-8
ANSWER: The head of John the Baptist

SPACES AWARDED: 3

QUESTION: What did Jesus feed to the 4000 people who came to hear Him preach?

REFERENCE: Matthew 15:36
ANSWER: Loaves (bread) and fish

SPACES AWARDED: 2

QUESTION: What did Jesus tell Peter to catch, then open its mouth to find money to pay their temple tax?

REFERENCE: Matthew 17:27
ANSWER: A fish

SPACES AWARDED: 3

QUESTION: According to Matthew 6:20, where should Christians store up treasures?

REFERENCE: Matthew 6:20
ANSWER: In heaven

SPACES AWARDED: 2

QUESTION: Which gate leads to destruction, the narrow gate or the wide gate?

REFERENCE: Matthew 7:13
ANSWER: The wide gate

SPACES AWARDED: 1

QUESTION: According to Matthew 5, Christians are to be
a. bread and light
b. fishers of men
c. salt and light

REFERENCE: Matthew 5:13-14
ANSWER: c. salt and light

SPACES AWARDED: 2

QUESTION: In what town was Jesus born?

REFERENCE: Matthew 2:1
ANSWER: Bethlehem

SPACES AWARDED: 2

QUESTION: Where did the angel command Joseph to take Jesus to keep Him safe from Herod?

REFERENCE: Matthew 2:13
ANSWER: Egypt

SPACES AWARDED: 3

QUESTION: According to Matthew 12:34, what you speak starts first in your
a. mouth.
b. heart.
c. brain.

REFERENCE: Matthew 12:34
ANSWER: b. heart

SPACES AWARDED: 1

SS3842

SS3842

QUESTION: According to Matthew 10:30, God knows exactly how many ____ are on your head.

REFERENCE: Matthew 10:30

ANSWER: hairs

SPACES AWARDED: 2

QUESTION: God says He will reward Christians for giving a cup of ____ to someone in need.

REFERENCE: Matthew 10:42

ANSWER: cold water

SPACES AWARDED: 2

QUESTION: The people of what town knew Jesus as the carpenter's son and did not honor Him?

REFERENCE: Matthew 13:53-57

ANSWER: His hometown—Nazareth

SPACES AWARDED: 4

QUESTION: What animal did Jesus say would be easier to put through a needle's eye than for a rich man to enter the kingdom?

REFERENCE: Matthew 19:24

ANSWER: A camel

SPACES AWARDED: 3

QUESTION: In which city did Jesus tell His disciples He would be crucified?

REFERENCE: Matthew 20:17-19

ANSWER: Jerusalem

SPACES AWARDED: 2

QUESTION: Jesus said you must first be a ____ before you can become a great person.

REFERENCE: Matthew 20:26

ANSWER: servant

SPACES AWARDED: 3

QUESTION: What animal did Jesus ask His disciples to get for Him to ride into Jerusalem?

REFERENCE: Matthew 21:2

ANSWER: A donkey or colt

SPACES AWARDED: 2

QUESTION: What kind of tree did Jesus cause to wither because it didn't have fruit?

REFERENCE: Matthew 21:19

ANSWER: Fig tree

SPACES AWARDED: 4

QUESTION: Where was Jesus when a woman anointed Him with expensive perfume?

REFERENCE: Matthew 26:6-7

ANSWER: Bethany

SPACES AWARDED: 4

SS3842

SS3842

QUESTION: What was the jar made of that held the perfume used by a woman to anoint Jesus?

REFERENCE: Matthew 26:6-8

ANSWER: Alabaster

SPACES AWARDED: 4

QUESTION: Where was Jesus when Judas betrayed Him?
a. An upper room
b. The Garden of Gethsemane
c. On His way to Jerusalem

REFERENCE: Matthew 26:36, 47-50

ANSWER: b. The Garden of Gethsemane

SPACES AWARDED: 2

QUESTION: True or False—The Field of Blood was a burial place purchased with the thirty coins that Judas returned to the chief priests.

REFERENCE: Matthew 27:3-8

ANSWER: True

SPACES AWARDED: 2

QUESTION: Name two of the three things the soldiers put on Jesus, shortly before His death.

REFERENCE: Matthew 27:28-29

ANSWER: A scarlet robe, a crown of thorns, a staff

SPACES AWARDED: 4

QUESTION: What did the soldiers force Simon of Cyrene to carry for Jesus?

REFERENCE: Matthew 27:32

ANSWER: His cross

SPACES AWARDED: 3

QUESTION: Where was Jesus crucified?

REFERENCE: Matthew 27:33

ANSWER: Golgotha

SPACES AWARDED: 4

QUESTION: What did someone offer Jesus to drink when He was dying on the cross?

REFERENCE: Matthew 27:48

ANSWER: wine vinegar

SPACES AWARDED: 3

QUESTION: Name one of the things done to assure that no one would break into Jesus' tomb and steal His body.

REFERENCE: Matthew 27:66

ANSWER: Put a seal on the stone or posted guards.

SPACES AWARDED: 4

QUESTION: According to the book of Mark, what did John the Baptist eat?

REFERENCE: Mark 1:6

ANSWER: Locusts and wild honey

SPACES AWARDED: 3

SS3842

SS3842

QUESTION: Where did Jesus' parents go every year for the Feast of the Passover?

REFERENCE: Luke 2:41
ANSWER: Jerusalem

SPACES AWARDED: 4

QUESTION: In Luke 7, what did the sinful woman use to wipe Jesus' feet?

REFERENCE: Luke 7:38
ANSWER: Her hair

SPACES AWARDED: 3

QUESTION: What part of the head did Jesus say He has numbered?

REFERENCE: Luke 12:7
ANSWER: Our hairs

SPACES AWARDED: 2

QUESTION: Jesus often compared the multitudes to
a. sheep.
b. goats.
c. wolves.

REFERENCE: Mark 6:34
ANSWER: a. sheep

SPACES AWARDED: 2

QUESTION: A begging mother told Jesus that even the ___ were allowed to eat the crumbs that fell from the table. What animal did she mention?

REFERENCE: Mark 7:28
ANSWER: dogs

SPACES AWARDED: 2

QUESTION: Where was Mary living when the angel told her she would be the mother of Jesus?

REFERENCE: Luke 1:26
ANSWER: Nazareth (in Galilee)

SPACES AWARDED: 3

QUESTION: In what river did John baptize Jesus?

REFERENCE: Mark 1:9
ANSWER: Jordan River

SPACES AWARDED: 4

QUESTION: What sea was Jesus walking beside when He called Simon and Andrew to be His disciples?

REFERENCE: Mark 1:16
ANSWER: Sea of Galilee

SPACES AWARDED: 4

QUESTION: True or False–The disciples were to take food, luggage, and money on their journey when Jesus sent them out.

REFERENCE: Mark 6:8
ANSWER: False

SPACES AWARDED: 2

SS3842

SS3842

QUESTION: Judas Iscariot was known as "keeper of the _____".

REFERENCE: John 12:6
ANSWER: money bag

SPACES AWARDED: 2

QUESTION: When Jesus entered Jerusalem on a donkey, what did the people wave at Him?

REFERENCE: John 12:13
ANSWER: Palm branches

SPACES AWARDED: 2

QUESTION: According to John 14:27, what does Jesus give that the world can't give?

REFERENCE: John 14:27
ANSWER: Peace

SPACES AWARDED: 2

QUESTION: According to John 8:32, knowing the _____ sets people free.

REFERENCE: John 8:32
ANSWER: truth

SPACES AWARDED: 3

QUESTION: What did Jesus put on the blind man's eyes when He healed him?

REFERENCE: John 9:6
ANSWER: Mud

SPACES AWARDED: 2

QUESTION: Mary, Martha, and Lazarus lived in what village?

REFERENCE: John 11:1
ANSWER: Bethany

SPACES AWARDED: 3

QUESTION: What flowers did Jesus tell the disciples to "consider," because God takes care of them?

REFERENCE: Luke 12:27
ANSWER: The lilies

SPACES AWARDED: 3

QUESTION: What did Jesus ask the Samaritan woman to give Him?

REFERENCE: John 4:7
ANSWER: A drink

SPACES AWARDED: 3

QUESTION: In what city is the pool of Bethesda located?
a. Bethlehem
b. Jerusalem
c. Jericho

REFERENCE: John 5:2
ANSWER: b. Jerusalem

SPACES AWARDED: 4

SS3842

SS3842

QUESTION: The Berean Christians were noble because they studied what daily?

REFERENCE: Acts 17:11
ANSWER: The Scriptures (God's Word)

SPACES AWARDED: 3

QUESTION: What city did Paul visit that was full of idols?
a. Athens
b. Corinth
c. Berea

REFERENCE: Acts 17:16
ANSWER: a. Athens

SPACES AWARDED: 2

QUESTION: According to Acts 27:14, what is a "wind of hurricane force" called?

REFERENCE: Acts 27:14
ANSWER: A "northeaster"

SPACES AWARDED: 4

QUESTION: Saul, who later became the Apostle Paul, was from
a. Tarsus.
b. Jerusalem.
c. Damascus.

REFERENCE: Acts 9:11
ANSWER: a. Tarsus

SPACES AWARDED: 2

QUESTION: True or False—Persecution of Christians in Jerusalem caused them to be scattered into Judea and Samaria.

REFERENCE: Acts 8:1
ANSWER: True

SPACES AWARDED: 2

QUESTION: In Lystra, Paul was
a. shipwrecked.
b. stoned and left for dead.
c. beaten by soldiers.

REFERENCE: Acts 14:8, 19
ANSWER: b. stoned and left for dead

SPACES AWARDED: 2

QUESTION: True or False—Disciples (Christians) belong to the world.

REFERENCE: John 15:19
ANSWER: False

SPACES AWARDED: 1

QUESTION: What did Judas Iscariot buy with the money he got for betraying Jesus?

REFERENCE: Acts 1:18
ANSWER: A field (some land)

SPACES AWARDED: 4

QUESTION: What was the Ethiopian man reading when Philip ran up to his chariot?

REFERENCE: Acts 8:30
ANSWER: The book of Isaiah the prophet

SPACES AWARDED: 4

SS3842

QUESTION: According to 1 Timothy 6:7, are we going to take anything with us when we leave this world?

REFERENCE: 1 Timothy 6:7
ANSWER: No

SPACES AWARDED: 1

QUESTION: 1 Timothy 6:8 says we should be content if we have what two things?

REFERENCE: 1 Timothy 6:8
ANSWER: Food and clothing

SPACES AWARDED: 2

QUESTION: The streets in the Holy City (Jerusalem) are made from what precious metal?

REFERENCE: Revelation 21:21
ANSWER: Pure gold

SPACES AWARDED: 3

QUESTION: What kind of giver does the Lord love?

REFERENCE: 2 Corinthians 9:7
ANSWER: A cheerful one

SPACES AWARDED: 2

QUESTION: According to Ephesians 2:8-9, are we saved by grace or by works?

REFERENCE: Ephesians 2:8-9
ANSWER: By grace

SPACES AWARDED: 2

QUESTION: True or False–According to Ephesians 4:25, it is all right to tell a lie to your neighbor.

REFERENCE: Ephesians 4:25
ANSWER: False

SPACES AWARDED: 2

QUESTION: What came out of the wood that Paul gathered for a fire?

REFERENCE: Acts 28:3
ANSWER: A viper (snake)

SPACES AWARDED: 2

QUESTION: Which is the greatest–hope, faith, or love?

REFERENCE: 1 Corinthians 13:13
ANSWER: Love

SPACES AWARDED: 1

QUESTION: What will sound (make a noise) just before the dead in Christ are raised?

REFERENCE: 1 Corinthians 15:52
ANSWER: The trumpet

SPACES AWARDED: 3

SS3842

SS3842

QUESTION: Which parable talks about seeds, soil, birds, and thorns?
a. The mustard seed
b. The hidden treasure
c. The sower

REFERENCE: Matthew 13:3-8
ANSWER: c. The sower

SPACES AWARDED: 2

QUESTION: Which parable talks about weeds, wheat, and fire?
a. The mustard seed
b. The weeds
c. The lost pearl

REFERENCE: Matthew 13:24-30
ANSWER: b. The weeds

SPACES AWARDED: 3

QUESTION: Which parable talks about a lake, fish, fishermen, and baskets?
a. The net
b. The pearl
c. The yeast

REFERENCE: Matthew 13:47-52
ANSWER: a. The net

SPACES AWARDED: 2

QUESTION: Jesus said to "____ your enemies and ____ for those who persecute you."

REFERENCE: Matthew 5:44
ANSWER: love/pray

SPACES AWARDED: 2

QUESTION: "But seek first his ____ and his ____, and all these ____ will be given to you as well."

REFERENCE: Matthew 6:33
ANSWER: kingdom/righteousness/things

SPACES AWARDED: 4

QUESTION: Jesus said, "Come to me, all you who are weary and burdened, and ____ ____."

REFERENCE: Matthew 11:28
ANSWER: I will give you rest

SPACES AWARDED: 3

QUESTION: "God with us" is the meaning of the name
a. Jesus.
b. Immanuel.
c. Jehovah.

REFERENCE: Matthew 1:23
ANSWER: b. Immanuel

SPACES AWARDED: 2

QUESTION: Who said, "Where is the . . . king of the Jews? We saw his star in the east and have come to worship him."

REFERENCE: Matthew 2:1-2
ANSWER: The magi (wise men)

SPACES AWARDED: 3

QUESTION: ". . . ____ does not live on ____ alone, but on every ____ that comes from the mouth of God."

REFERENCE: Matthew 4:4
ANSWER: Man/bread/word

SPACES AWARDED: 2

SS3842

SS3842

QUESTION: In the parable of the two sons, which son went out to work in the vineyard–the first or the second?

REFERENCE: Matthew 21:28-31
ANSWER: The first son

SPACES AWARDED: 2

QUESTION: In the parable of the tenants, the tenants
a. killed the owner's son.
b. Honored the owner's son.
c. held the owner's son hostage.

REFERENCE: Matthew 21:33-39
ANSWER: a. killed the owner's son.

SPACES AWARDED: 2

QUESTION: True or False–The parable of the wedding banquet teaches us that everyone can come to the banquet.

REFERENCE: Matthew 22:14
ANSWER: False ("For many are invited, but few are chosen.")

SPACES AWARDED: 3

QUESTION: The parable of the unmerciful ___ teaches us that we should forgive others from our heart.

REFERENCE: Matthew 18:23-35
ANSWER: servant

SPACES AWARDED: 2

QUESTION: Jesus said, "Therefore what ___ has joined together, let ___ not separate."

REFERENCE: Matthew 19:6
ANSWER: God / man

SPACES AWARDED: 3

QUESTION: True or False–The parable of the workers in the vineyard teaches that the landowner was generous in paying all the workers equally, whether they worked all day or part of the day.

REFERENCE: Matthew 20:9-15
ANSWER: True

SPACES AWARDED: 2

QUESTION: "For whoever does the will of my Father in heaven is my ___ and sister and ___."

REFERENCE: Matthew 12:50
ANSWER: brother / mother

SPACES AWARDED: 2

QUESTION: "Therefore, whoever ___ himself like this ___ is the greatest in the kingdom of ___."

REFERENCE: Matthew 18:4
ANSWER: humbles / child / heaven

SPACES AWARDED: 4

QUESTION: Which parable talks about a sheep and a shepherd?
a. The workers in the vineyard
b. The lost sheep
c. The two sons

REFERENCE: Matthew 18:10-14
ANSWER: b. The lost sheep

SPACES AWARDED: 1

Shining Star Publications, Copyright © 1994

SS3842

52

SS3842

QUESTION: Jesus said to Simon and Andrew, "Come, follow me, and I will make you ___ ___."

REFERENCE: Mark 1:17
ANSWER: fishers of men

SPACES AWARDED: 3

QUESTION: In the parable of the sower, who is the one who sows the Word?

REFERENCE: Mark 4:14
ANSWER: The farmer (the sower)

SPACES AWARDED: 3

QUESTION: In the parable of the mustard seed, to what did Jesus compare the kingdom of God?

REFERENCE: Mark 4:30-31
ANSWER: A mustard seed

SPACES AWARDED: 2

QUESTION: Soldiers mocked Jesus at His trial by saying, "Hail, ___ ___!"

REFERENCE: Matthew 27:29
ANSWER: king of the Jews

SPACES AWARDED: 3

QUESTION: These are words Jesus cried out on the cross to His Father: "My God, my God, why have ___ ___?"

REFERENCE: Matthew 27:46
ANSWER: you forsaken me

SPACES AWARDED: 3

QUESTION: Jesus said, "Go and make disciples of all nations, ___ them in the name of the Father and of the Son and of the ___ Spirit."

REFERENCE: Matthew 28:19
ANSWER: baptizing/Holy

SPACES AWARDED: 2

QUESTION: "For whoever exalts himself will be humbled, and whoever ___ himself will be ___."

REFERENCE: Matthew 23:12
ANSWER: humbles/exalted

SPACES: 2

QUESTION: "Heaven and earth will pass away, but my ___ will never ___."

REFERENCE: Matthew 24:35
ANSWER: words/pass away

SPACES AWARDED: 3

QUESTION: Which parable teaches us to watch for the Master's return?
a. The talents
b. The sheep and the goats
c. The ten virgins

REFERENCE: Matthew 25:1-13
ANSWER: c. The ten virgins

SPACES AWARDED: 2

SS3842

QUESTION: Jesus quoted this verse from the book of Isaiah: "These people honor me with their ___, but their ___ are far from me."

REFERENCE: Mark 7:6
ANSWER: lips/hearts

SPACES AWARDED: 3

QUESTION: Jesus said: "If anyone would ___ after me, he must deny ___ and take up his ___ and ___ me."

REFERENCE: Mark 8:34
ANSWER: come/himself/cross/follow

SPACES AWARDED: 4

QUESTION: Jesus said, "And when you stand ___ if you hold anything against anyone, ___ him, so that your ___ in heaven may forgive you your sins."

REFERENCE: Mark 11:25
ANSWER: praying/forgive/Father

SPACES AWARDED: 3

QUESTION: What should you do "with all your heart, soul, mind, and strength"?

REFERENCE: Mark 12:30
ANSWER: "Love the Lord your God."

SPACES AWARDED: 4

QUESTION: "Heaven and earth will pass away, but my ___ ___ ___."

REFERENCE: Mark 13:31
ANSWER: words will never pass away

SPACES AWARDED: 4

QUESTION: At Jesus' death the centurion said, Surely this man was the ___ of ___!"

REFERENCE: Mark 15:39
ANSWER: Son/God

SPACES AWARDED: 2

QUESTION: Mary said, "The Mighty One has done ___ things for me—holy is his ___."

REFERENCE: Luke 1:49
ANSWER: great/name

SPACES AWARDED: 3

QUESTION: "And ___ grew in wisdom and stature, and in favor with ___ and men."

REFERENCE: Luke 2:52
ANSWER: Jesus/God

SPACES AWARDED: 2

QUESTION: Jesus said, "Blessed rather are those who ___ the word of God and ___ it."

REFERENCE: Luke 11:28
ANSWER: hear/obey

SPACES AWARDED: 2

SS3842

QUESTION: Which parable teaches us not to store up riches for ourselves and forget God?
a. The ten virgins
b. The sheep and the goats
c. The rich fool

REFERENCE: Luke 12:13-21
ANSWER: c. The rich fool

SPACES AWARDED: 2

QUESTION: Give one of the three excuses an invited guest gave in the parable of the great banquet.

REFERENCE: Luke 14:18-2o
ANSWER: "I bought a field, I bought oxen, or I just got married."

SPACES AWARDED: 4

QUESTION: In the parable of the lost son, who was waiting for the son to return?

REFERENCE: Luke 15:20
ANSWER: His father

SPACES AWARDED: 2

QUESTION: This is the right that God gives to all who believe in Jesus—to become ___ of God."

REFERENCE: John 1:12
ANSWER: children

SPACES AWARDED: 2

QUESTION: Jesus said, "I am the ___ of the world. Whoever follows me will never walk in ___."

REFERENCE: John 8:12
ANSWER: light/darkness

SPACES AWARDED: 3

QUESTION: This was said of the Pharisees: "They loved ___ from men more than praise from ___."

REFERENCE: John 12:43
ANSWER: praise/God

SPACES AWARDED: 2

QUESTION: Jesus said, "No ___ is greater than his master."

REFERENCE: John 13:16
ANSWER: servant

SPACES AWARDED: 1

QUESTION: Jesus said, "I am the ___ the ___ and the life. No one comes to the ___ except through me."

REFERENCE: John 14:6
ANSWER: way/truth/Father

SPACES AWARDED: 3

QUESTION: Peter and the apostles told those who arrested them, "We must ___ God rather than ___!"

REFERENCE: Acts 5:29
ANSWER: obey/men

SPACES AWARDED: 2

SS3842

QUESTION: Paul said, "There is ___ one righteous, not even ___."

REFERENCE: Romans 3:10
ANSWER: no/one

SPACES AWARDED: 2

QUESTION: "While we were still sinners, Christ ___."

REFERENCE: Romans 5:8
ANSWER: died for us

SPACES AWARDED: 3

QUESTION: "For the wages of ___ is death, but the ___ of God is ___."

REFERENCE: Romans 6:23
ANSWER: sin/gift/eternal life

SPACES AWARDED: 4

QUESTION: According to Romans 8:39, what can "separate us from the love of God"?

REFERENCE: Romans 8:39
ANSWER: Nothing

SPACES AWARDED: 1

QUESTION: "If you confess with your mouth, 'Jesus is Lord,' and believe in ___ that God raised him from the dead, you will be ___."

REFERENCE: Romans 10:9
ANSWER: your heart/saved

SPACES AWARDED: 3

QUESTION: According to Romans 14:12, who will "give an account of himself to God"?

REFERENCE: Romans 14:12
ANSWER: each of us (everyone)

SPACES AWARDED: 2

QUESTION: "Bad ___ corrupts good character."

REFERENCE: 1 Corinthians 15:33
ANSWER: company

SPACES AWARDED: 2

QUESTION: God comforts us so that we can " ___ those . . . with the comfort we ourselves have received from ___."

REFERENCE: 2 Corinthians 1:4
ANSWER: comfort/God

SPACES AWARDED: 2

QUESTION: True or False—Galatians 5:17 teaches that our sinful nature fights against our spiritual nature.

REFERENCE: Galatians 5:17
ANSWER: True

SPACES AWARDED: 1

SS3842

SS3842

QUESTION: "The Lord . . . is patient . . . not wanting anyone to ___, but everyone to come to ___."

REFERENCE: 2 Peter 3:9
ANSWER: perish/repentance

SPACES AWARDED: 2

QUESTION: Which book of the Bible promises a special blessing to everyone who reads it?

REFERENCE: Revelation 1:3
ANSWER: Revelation

SPACES AWARDED: 3

QUESTION: "And God will ___ away every ___ from their eyes."

REFERENCE: Revelation 7:17
ANSWER: wipe/tear

SPACES AWARDED: 2

QUESTION: "For the love of ___ is a root of all kinds of ___."

REFERENCE: 1 Timothy 6:10
ANSWER: money/evil

SPACES AWARDED: 2

QUESTION: "For ___ did not give us a spirit of timidity, but a spirit of ___."

REFERENCE: 2 Timothy 1:7
ANSWER: God/power

SPACES AWARDED: 2

QUESTION: "Submit yourselves, then, to ___. Resist the ___, and he will flee from you."

REFERENCE: James 4:7
ANSWER: God/devil

SPACES AWARDED: 3

QUESTION: "God cannot be mocked. A man reaps ___."

REFERENCE: Galatians 6:7
ANSWER: what he sows

SPACES AWARDED: 3

QUESTION: "Speak to one another with ___, ___ and spiritual ___."

REFERENCE: Ephesians 5:19
ANSWER: psalms, hymns, songs

SPACES AWARDED: 3

QUESTION: "Set your minds on ___, not on earthly ___."

REFERENCE: Colossians 3:2
ANSWER: things above/things

SPACES AWARDED: 3

SS3842

SS3842

SS3842